CREDO

STUDY JOURNAL

This Journal Belongs To:

_____

Excerpts from Bishop Athanasius Schneider's *Credo: Compendium of the Catholic Faith* (Manchester: Sophia Institute Press, 2023) have been reproduced here with the author's permission, and are indicated by shortened page number references throughout.

Liturgical text excerpts are included from the approved Latin-English edition of *The New Roman Missal* (New York: Benziger Brothers, 1945) by Fr. Francis Xavier Lasance, available in the public domain.

Printed in the United States of America. All rights reserved.

Cover design by Perceptions Studio

Front cover art: Basilica of the Holy Cross in Jerusalem. *Christ the Pantocrator*, by Antoniazzo Romano and Marco Palmezzano (ca. 1480). (DAE-97026879) © agefotostock.com: De Agostini / G. Cargagna

Sophia Institute Press
Box 5284, Manchester, NH 03108
1-800-888-9344
www.SophiaInstitute.com

Sophia Institute Press is a registered trademark of Sophia Institute.

ISBN 979-8-88911-170-2

eBook ISBN 979-8-88911-171-9

Library of Congress Control Number: 2023942497

first edition

How to Use This Journal

Laudetur Iesus Christus — Praised be Jesus Christ!

Bishop Athanasius Schneider has done a great service to men and women everywhere by publishing *Credo: Compendium of the Catholic Faith* (Manchester: Sophia Institute Press, 2023), here cited simply as *Credo*.

    As a succinct but wide-ranging summary of the faith, morals, and worship of the Catholic Church, *Credo* is a bold presentation of timeless truths, and a help for Catholics and non-Catholics alike — engaging current issues in the clear light of the gospel, and offering an invaluable aid for anyone seeking to grow closer to God.

    This *Study Journal* has been compiled as a companion resource to Bishop Schneider's *Credo*, to further assist in its fruitful reception and use in various settings. It is designed to serve individual readers as well as study groups, classroom instructors, retreat programs, and large-format presentations, with each spread following its corresponding chapter in *Credo*. Note-taking space is included throughout, along with these recurring elements:

    Study » *Key concepts that highlight each chapter's main doctrinal points*

    Reflect » *Prompts to help readers apply chapter themes to their own lives*

    Discuss » *Topically related prompts to encourage group discussion*

    Lex Orandi » *Prayer from the Roman Missal reflecting a chapter topic*

    Lex Credendi » *Chapter excerpt from* **Credo** *illustrating the same topic*

Let this *Journal* deepen your own personal growth in faith, guide your study group, enrich your catechism class, or shape your homilies — drawing on the text of Bishop Schneider's invaluable *Compendium of the Catholic Faith*.

May God richly bless your study of Catholicism,
and draw you ever deeper into the life
of grace and holiness available within it.

Introduction

STUDY

- Christian
- Catholic
- sign of the cross
- revelation
- doctrine
- dogma
- Sacred Scripture
- Old Testament
- New Testament
- Sacred Tradition
- Magisterium
- canon

REFLECT

- What is the great dignity of the Christian?
- Am I a true Catholic? If not, why not?
- Is Christian faith more than merely "belief"?

DISCUSS

- How can we act for our neighbor's good?
- Can there be any errors in Sacred Scripture?
- Have you encountered any of the "principal errors" against divine revelation? If so, what was your response?

LEX CREDENDI

"What is divine revelation? Revelation is a supernatural communication that occurred publicly in human history, in which God has revealed Himself and shown what man must know, believe, and do to live well on earth and be united to God forever in the bliss of heaven. Jesus Christ, the Incarnate Word of God, Himself is the fullness of divine revelation: 'The only-begotten Son who is in the bosom of the Father, He has made Him known' (Jn 1:18)." — *Credo*, 2

LEX ORANDI

"Almighty, eternal God, Who hast revealed in Christ Thy glory to all the nations, guard the works of Thy mercy; that Thy Church, spread throughout the whole earth, may with steadfast faith persevere in the confession of Thy name." — Collect, Good Friday

Part I, Chapter 1: God

STUDY

- natural reason
- Motion
- Efficient Causality
- Contingency
- Gradation
- Finality and Order
- nature
- divine nature
- divine attributes
- providence

REFLECT

- Which divine attribute is the most difficult to comprehend?
- Have I doubted God's providence?
- Do I trust God when He permits suffering in my life?

DISCUSS

- What is your favorite logical proof for the existence of God?
- How should we respond to those who publicly profess to be atheists?
- What is the problem of evil? How can it be answered?

"Who is God? The one uncreated, pure, and perfect spirit, the source and master of all things, 'Creator and Lord of heaven and earth, almighty, eternal, immeasurable, incomprehensible, infinite in understanding, will, and every perfection.'" — *Credo*, 13

_____

_____

_____

_____

_____

_____

_____

_____

_____

_____

_____

_____

_____

_____

_____

_____

_____

Lex Orandi

"I believe in one God, the Father Almighty, Maker of heaven and earth, and of all things visible and invisible." —Nicene Creed, Ordinary of Mass

Part I, Chapter 2: The Blessed Trinity

STUDY

- mystery
- Blessed Trinity
- Father
- Son
- Holy Spirit
- consubstantial
- personal properties
- external actions
- suprarational
- incomprehensible

REFLECT

- How do I approach my own study of Catholicism?
- Do I begin each day with some act of adoration to the Blessed Trinity?
- Why is the dogma of the Trinity so essential to right faith?

DISCUSS

- What are some good examples of *natural mysteries*?
- Do you understand Augustine's analogy for the Trinity? What are some others you may have heard? How are they adequate (or inadequate)?
- Have you encountered any of the "principal religious errors" about the Trinity? How can we effectively share the truth with those that hold such errors?

"What is the mystery of the Blessed Trinity? Meaning 'the holy Three,' the Blessed Trinity is the mystery of one God in three distinct but co-equal Persons: Father, Son, and Holy Spirit." — *Credo*, 18

Lex Orandi

"With all our hearts we confess Thee, we praise Thee, we bless Thee, God the Father unbegotten, Thee, the only-begotten Son, Thee, the Holy Ghost, the Paraclete, holy and undivided Trinity." —Tract, Votive Mass of the Most Holy Trinity

Part I, Chapter 3: Creation

STUDY

- *ex nihilo*
- emanation
- transhumanism
- six days
- "end" of creation
- anthropocentrism

REFLECT

- God created *ex nihilo*, and did not "need" to create me; does this truth move me to humility and gratitude?
- How am I prone to *anthropocentrism* in my own thoughts or actions?
- What circumstances of my life am I using well, "as means to rise to God"?

DISCUSS

- How are some claims of the natural sciences—especially about origins—really errors of philosophy?
- How does *transhumanism* reflect the sin of our first parents?
- What are some concrete ways that we can fulfill our duties toward other creatures?

Lex Credendi

"What has God revealed to man about His work of Creation? In the divinely revealed history especially contained in the book of Genesis, this work is described as God calling the universe into existence by His Almighty Word, and giving this creation a splendid order and harmony in a sequence of six days (see Gn 1:6–8, 14–19)." — *Credo*, 21

Lex Orandi

"In the beginning was the Word, and the Word was with God, and the Word was God. The same was in the beginning with God. All things were made by Him, and without Him was made nothing that was made." — Last Gospel, Ordinary of Mass

Part I, Chapter 4: The Angels

STUDY

- angel
- Beatific Vision
- salvation
- choirs
- guardian angels
- Satan
- demons
- temptation
- obsession
- possession

REFLECT

- How have I been faithful in my duties toward my guardian angel?
- Am I confident that, by God's grace, I can "always overcome the assaults of the devil"?
- How can I be a truer friend of the angels, and a more effective enemy of the demons?

DISCUSS

- Why is the angelic nature superior to that of man?
- Have you ever witnessed God drawing good even out of the attacks of the devil?
- Explain why it is always wrong to claim, "The devil made me do it!"

LEX CREDENDI

"What is an angel? Meaning 'messenger,' an angel is a pure spirit, a being of personal intelligence and will, created by God to glorify and serve Him." — *Credo*, 22

LEX ORANDI

"O God, Who dost in wonderful order dispose the ministries of angels and men, mercifully grant that our lives be fortified by those who continually stand in Thy presence and minister before Thee in heaven." —Collect, Dedication of St. Michael the Archangel

Part I, Chapter 5: Man

STUDY

- man
- Adam
- body-soul unity
- soul
- Eve
- immortal
- evolution
- polygenism
- original justice
- Fall of man
- Original Sin

REFLECT

- Why did God create man? Have I committed the answer to memory?
- Do I believe that Heaven is owed to me, or that I will certainly attain it?
- What trials in my life could be used as demonstrations of my love for God?

DISCUSS

- What signs of *materialism* are commonly encountered in society today?
- How does the error of "gender ideology" place man above God?
- What problems arise from denying the unity of the human race in the original human pair of Adam and Eve?

LEX CREDENDI

"What name was given to the first man? The first man was called *Adam* (reddish clay), evoking the humble origin of his body." — *Credo*, 26

LEX ORANDI

"Remember, O man, that thou art dust, and unto dust thou shalt return." —Admonition, Ash Wednesday

Part I, Chapter 6: The Messiah Promised

STUDY

- Messiah
- religion
- natural religion
- supernatural religion
- false religion(s)
- religious indifferentism
- evangelization
- human dignity
- human fraternity

REFLECT

- I will meditate on the divine mercy and generosity of God, in promising us a Redeemer.
- Do I see *evangelization* as an act of love? Do I actively pray and work for it?
- God waited for "the fullness of time" before sending a Redeemer; am I waiting for anything from God? If so, am I waiting well?

DISCUSS

- Several specific religious errors are addressed in this chapter; which of them stand out?
- How should we pray and work for the conversion of non-Catholics?
- How should we understand authentic human dignity? What kind of fraternity should we seek after?

Lex Credendi

"Then God did not abandon man after the Fall? No. God's love for man prepared a way to reconcile His mercy with His justice through the mission of the Messiah—Jesus Christ—who could make a satisfaction more than equal to the offense." — *Credo*, 32

Lex Orandi

"I will put enmities between thee and the Woman, and between thy seed and her Seed." —Offertory, Assumption of the Blessed Virgin Mary

Part I, Chapter 7: The Messiah Prepared For

STUDY

- types (persons, objects, events)
- prophecy
- major prophets
- minor prophets
- Messianic prophecies

REFLECT

- Considering the humble obedience of Our Lord in carrying the Cross, how may I carry my cross with greater merit?
- In what way(s) am I offering myself as a sacrifice for others?
- Poverty is a great virtue of the Messiah; is there anything I'm unwilling to give up or let go of?

DISCUSS

- Why is *prophecy* such a major aspect of God's revelation?
- Were you familiar with the various "types" of the Messiah before? Which is your favorite?
- Why was the foretelling of Christ's Passion especially important for Christians of all times?

"What is a *Messianic* prophecy? Any prophecy referring to the Messiah, announcing the events of the Gospel before they occurred." — *Credo*, 41

LEX ORANDI

"There shall come forth a rod out of the root of Jesse, and a Sower shall rise up out of his root. And the Spirit of the Lord shall rest upon Him." — Gradual, Maternity of the Blessed Virgin Mary

Part I, Chapter 8: The Incarnation

STUDY

- Incarnation
- Jesus
- Christ
- threefold anointing (King, High Priest, Prophet)
- divine nature
- human nature
- hypostatic union
- Arianism

REFLECT

- What does the name *Jesus* really mean to me? If I call Him "Lord," do my actions and attitude reflect this?
- The sinless Christ chose to suffer for love of me; how do I choose to suffer for love of Him?
- Does my human will reflect Christ's human will? If not, why not?

DISCUSS

- How did Our Lord prove His divinity? Why aren't these proofs universally believed?
- Wars were fought over the early heresies surrounding the Incarnation. Why is this dogma so essential to Christianity?
- How is every departure from Catholic doctrine "essentially an error about the Incarnation"?

LEX CREDENDI

"What is this mystery called? This mystery is called the *Incarnation*, when the Eternal Son of God united to Himself a complete human nature in the one divine Person named Jesus Christ: 'True God was born in the complete and perfect nature of true man; completely human and completely divine.'" — *Credo*, 43

LEX ORANDI

"Confirm, O Lord, in our minds, we beseech Thee, the mysteries of the true Faith; that we who confess Him Who was conceived of a Virgin to be true God and man, may deserve to arrive at eternal joy, by the power of His saving Resurrection." —Secret, Annunciation of the Blessed Virgin Mary

Part I, Chapter 9: The Blessed Virgin

STUDY

- Virgin Mary
- Annunciation
- Immaculate Conception
- divine maternity
- perpetual virginity
- Assumption
- Coredemptrix
- Mediatrix

REFLECT

- Is Mary my mother? What difference does her spiritual motherhood make in my life?
- Why would it be fitting for Mary to die? Would I be willing to die, in imitation of Christ?
- What forms of Marian devotion do I practice? What others might I undertake this year?

DISCUSS

- Contrary to "the Church's constant teaching and liturgy," many popular portrayals of Our Lady show her experiencing pains in childbirth; why do you think this is?
- What is Our Lady's special mission in the Church, and how can we further it?
- Compare and contrast the roles that Adam and Eve played in the Fall of man with the roles that Jesus and Mary played in the Redemption of man.

LEX CREDENDI

"Why is Mary called our *Coredemptrix*? Because she cooperated in our salvation by agreeing to be Mother of the Redeemer, consenting to all His redeeming acts, and jointly offering His life to God on the Cross. 'The Redeemer could not but associate His Mother in His work. For this reason we invoke her under the title of Coredemptrix. She gave us the Savior, she accompanied Him in the work of Redemption as far as the Cross itself, sharing with Him the sorrows of the agony and of the death in which Jesus consummated the Redemption of mankind.'" — *Credo*, 49

LEX ORANDI

"O most merciful God, Who hast willed that the blessed Virgin Mary should be the Mother of Thine only-begotten Son and the administratrix of His graces for the salvation of sinners and a refuge of the wretched, grant, we beseech Thee, that, while we celebrate the festival of the heart of the same most loving Mother, we may be worthy to obtain both the conversion of sinners and an abundance of heavenly gifts for all the faithful." —Collect, Immaculate Heart of Mary

Part I, Chapter 10: The Life of Christ

STUDY

- hidden life
- Magi
- John the Baptist
- public life
- apostles
- mortification
- parables
- miracles

REFLECT

- I will meditate on the mystery of that first Christmas in Bethlehem. Like Jesus, am I "meek and humble of heart"?
- Jesus chose the weak and unimportant to be His apostles. What task has He called me to undertake with excellence, confident in His grace?
- Do I believe the miracles recorded in the Gospels? Do I believe that the followers of Jesus can do "greater works than these" (Jn 14:12) by His power?

DISCUSS

- Why did Jesus spend most of His years on earth in relative obscurity?
- Unlike other "religious figures" in human history, how did Jesus maintain and demonstrate His own unique and divine identity?
- How do you experience the Christian life as "one of prayer and combat"?

Lex Credendi

"How did God immediately prepare the Jews for the mission of the Savior? He sent St. John the Baptist as His precursor, the son of Zachary and Elizabeth, who prepared the way for Our Lord." — *Credo*, 52

Lex Orandi

"At that time, John saw Jesus coming to him, and he saith, Behold the Lamb of God, behold Him Who taketh away the sins of the world. This is He of Whom I said, After me there cometh a man, Who is preferred before me, because He was before me." —Gospel, Octave-Day of the Epiphany

Part I, Chapter 11: The Passion

STUDY

- Passion
- Garden of Olives
- Golgotha
- Seven Last Words
- death
- burial
- Redemption
- atonement
- justification
- satisfaction (voluntary, equivalent, superabundant, universal)

REFLECT

- I will meditate on the suffering endured by Our Lord, simply to show His love for me.
- On the Cross, Jesus endured the shame of abandonment by those who claimed to love Him. How would I have behaved in their place?
- Are works of *reparation* a regular part of my spiritual life? If not, why not?

DISCUSS

- Many of the religious authorities in Jesus' time rejected Him. Why does earthly power and influence pose such a temptation to deny Christ?
- Have you ever encountered one of the "main errors about the Redemption"? How could we help free someone from such errors?
- Why is it unreasonable to think that, in the end, all people might go to heaven?

LEX CREDENDI

"From what has Christ freed us? He has freed us from the slavery of sin and the eternal death that results from sin, at the price of His own precious blood. Holy Scripture says: 'Having been freed from sin and enslaved to God, you derive your benefit, resulting in sanctification, and the outcome, eternal life' (Rom 6:22)." — *Credo*, 58

LEX ORANDI

"O Lord Jesus Christ, Son of the living God, Who at the sixth hour didst ascend the scaffold of the Cross for the Redemption of the world, and didst shed Thy Precious Blood for the remission of our sins, we humbly beseech Thee that after our death Thou grant us to enter the gates of paradise rejoicing." — Postcommunion, Votive Mass of the Passion

Part I, Chapter 12: The Resurrection

STUDY

- hell
- limbo of the Fathers
- Resurrection
- *Dies Dominica*
- glorified body
- apostolic testimony
- brightness, impassibility, agility, subtlety

REFLECT

- I will meditate on the final agony of Jesus, and the descent of His soul into hell.
- Do I consider sin to be a true slavery, and an infinite offense against God?
- If I were in the position of St. Thomas, would I have faith in the Resurrection without visible proofs?

DISCUSS

- The love of Jesus led Him to descend into hell for those awaiting the Redemption; what lengths would we go to, to remain faithful to His grace?
- Why is the historical, bodily Resurrection of Jesus "the very foundation of Christianity"?
- Why is the apostolic testimony about the Resurrection still credible today?

Lex Credendi

"Why is Our Lord's Resurrection of such great importance? It is of first importance because it is: 1. The foundation of our faith (see 1 Cor 15:14–17); 2. The means whereby the fruits of the Redemption are applied to us (see 1 Pt 1:3); 3. The model of our spiritual life (see Rom 6:4–11); 4. The cause of our future resurrection (see Rom 6:5)." — *Credo*, 62

Lex Orandi

"It profited us nothing to be born except that we might be redeemed. O wondrous condescension of Thy great kindness in our regard! O inestimable affection of charity: to redeem the slave, Thou didst give up the Son! O truly necessary sin of Adam, that is wiped out by the death of Christ! O happy fault, that was worthy to have such and so great a Redeemer!" — Exsultet, Holy Saturday

Part I, Chapter 13: The Ascension

STUDY

- Ascension
- right hand of God
- Kingship of Christ

REFLECT

- If I were one of the apostles, spending time with the risen Christ, what questions would I have asked? What can I ask Him now, in prayer?
- I will meditate on the glorious Ascension of Jesus into heaven.
- How am I working to extend the reign of Christ the King, here on earth?

DISCUSS

- Have you ever considered the days between the Resurrection and Ascension of Christ? Why is His direct instruction of the disciples so important for our own faith and worship, today?
- Now enthroned in heaven, where do we see evidence of Christ's continued presence on earth?
- How should the Kingship of Christ be recognized on earth, and what should we be doing to extend His reign in the sociopolitical sphere?

"How must the Kingship of Christ be acknowledged? 1. *Individually*, by our choice to believe His doctrine and obey His commands; 2. *Collectively*, by families and nations living in accord with the same doctrine and moral precepts; 3. *Privately*, by progressing in the interior life of holiness; 4. *Publicly*, by imitating, obeying, and adoring our King in all external actions." — *Credo*, 65

"Fed with this immortal nourishment, we beseech Thee, O Lord, that we who glory to fight under the standard of Christ the King, may forever reign with Him on the heavenly throne." — Postcommunion, Christ the King

Part I, Chapter 14: The Second Coming

STUDY

- particular judgment
- general judgment
- signs of the Second Coming
- Antichrist
- works of mercy

REFLECT

- I will meditate on the Second Coming and the return of Christ in glory.
- Does the idea of an exacting judgment at the end of time fill me with joy, or fear? Why?
- Do I see any signs of the Second Coming in my own time?

DISCUSS

- The Second Coming should be a subject of great joy and encouragement for Christians; but do many give it much thought? Why or why not?
- If Christ returned in glory at this very moment, would you be numbered among the sheep or the goats?
- Why does Christ delay His Second Coming, and final victory over sin and death?

Lex Credendi

"How will Christ come at the end of the world? Not as He did the first time, in humility and weakness; rather, He will come in all the splendor of His power and glory." — *Credo*, 66

_____

_____

_____

_____

_____

_____

_____

_____

_____

_____

_____

_____

_____

_____

Lex Orandi

"O God, Who dost gladden us year by year with the expectation of our Redemption, grant that we, who now with joy receive Thine only-begotten Son as our Redeemer, may behold Him also without fear, when He cometh as our Judge, our Lord Jesus Christ." —Collect, Christmas Eve

Part I, Chapter 15: The Holy Spirit

STUDY

- Holy Spirit
- Macedonianism
- tongues of fire
- mission of the Holy Spirit
- soul of the Church
- state of grace
- gifts of the Holy Spirit
- fruits of the Holy Spirit

REFLECT

- I will meditate on the first Pentecost, gathered in the upper room with the disciples.
- Do I experience my time on earth as "two different lives"? How might I deepen my own interior union with God, day by day?
- Do I pray much to the Holy Spirit, or ask for His inspiration? Which of His gifts or fruits do I most need in my life right now?

DISCUSS

- How is the state of grace "a greater miracle than the creation of the universe," and do we see this state as "infinitely more valuable than our earthly lives"?
- Of the gifts and fruits of the Holy Spirit, which do you find the most appealing or desirable, and why?
- Which of the "duties to the Holy Spirit" do you think need greater attention today, in our own lives? In the lives of the clergy?

"What is the mission of the Holy Spirit in the soul of the individual Christian? He is the principle of supernatural life in the soul, and is therefore called *Vivificans* in the Creed, or 'life-giving Spirit.'" — *Credo*, 70

LEX ORANDI

"Holy Spirit! Lord of light!
From Thy clear celestial height,
Thy pure, beaming radiance give:
Come, Thou, Father of the poor!
Come, with treasures which endure!
Come, Thou light of all that live!"
—Sequence, Pentecost Sunday

Part I, Chapter 16: The Church and the Communion of Saints

STUDY

- Catholic
- Church
- Mystical Body of Christ
- mission of the Church

- *Extra Ecclesiam Nulla Salus*
- marks of the Church
- clergy
- laity
- consecrated religious

- levels of assent
- temporal power
- spiritual power
- religious liberty
- communion of saints

REFLECT

- I will meditate on that great cloud of visible and invisible fellowship: the communion of saints.
- Am I a *living member* of Christ's Mystical Body, the Church? Why or why not?
- Do I understand the true mission of the Church? What am I doing to fulfill that mission in my own state of life?

DISCUSS

- Where do you find the mission of the Church being misunderstood, misrepresented, or opposed in the world today? Do you see this as the "mark of persecution"? Why or why not?
- How can scandalous examples and erroneous teachings can come from the pastors of the Church? Practically speaking, what should we do in such situations?
- What is the proper Catholic understanding of the relationship between Church and state? What about "religious liberty"?

"What is the *communion of saints*? It is the spiritual union, relationship, and sharing of spiritual goods among the members of the Church on earth, of the souls in purgatory, and of the saints in heaven." — *Credo*, 70

LEX ORANDI

"Be propitiated, O Lord, by our supplications for the souls of Thy servants and handmaids, whose anniversary is kept today, for whom we offer Thee the sacrifice of praise, that Thou vouchsafe to join them to the company of Thy saints." —Secret, Second Mass for All Souls Day

Part I, Chapter 17: The Forgiveness of Sins

STUDY

- power of forgiveness
- required dispositions
- eternal punishment
- temporal punishment
- indulgences

REFLECT

- I will meditate on the moment when Christ first gave His disciples the divine power to forgive sins.
- Am I confident that God can forgive any sin, even the most heinous of mine—or of others? On the other hand, do I run any risk of presumption?
- Have I done sufficient penance and reparation for my own past sins? Is there more I could undertake, for the spiritual benefit of others?

DISCUSS

- Why is it so important that God has given us "an external and sensible" means of being reconciled with Him?
- Some view the Catholic teaching on sin as overly negative, judgmental, or "unmerciful." How would you respond to such claims?
- Have you ever come across one of the "chief errors about the forgiveness of sins" in your own life? How did you respond?

"Was it only to His apostles that Christ gave the power of forgiving sins? No. In the person of the apostles, He gave this power to the priests of His Church for all time, so that man might always have an external and sensible means of reconciliation with God." — *Credo*, 109

_____

_____

_____

_____

_____

_____

_____

_____

_____

_____

_____

_____

_____

LEX ORANDI

"May Almighty God have mercy upon you, forgive you your sins, and bring you unto life everlasting.... May the almighty and merciful Lord grant you pardon, absolution, and remission of your sins." —Pre-Communion Absolution, Ordinary of Mass

Part I, Chapter 18: The Resurrection of the Body

STUDY

- general resurrection
- natural images of resurrection
- value of the human body
- qualities of risen bodies

REFLECT

- I will meditate on the last trumpet and the general resurrection.
- Do I treat my own body and the bodies of others as true temples of the Holy Spirit?
- Have I ever drawn someone's attention to the Second Coming? Why or why not?

DISCUSS

- Many people are increasingly separated from the natural world—does this affect our understanding of the general resurrection? Why or why not?
- How does the dogma of the resurrection reinforce the value of the human body?
- In the resurrection, will we recognize our friends and family?

Lex Credendi

"How is the general resurrection possible, since bodies corrupt over time? This poses no difficulty to the omnipotent God, who formed all matter from nothing and can refashion the same body from the same material as it once was. Even so, the resurrection at the end of time remains a mystery and the subject of wonder." — *Credo*, 111

Lex Orandi

"Do Thou, O Lord, increase our faith in the Resurrection, Thou that workest wonders in the relics of Thy saints: and make us partakers of that immortal glory, a pledge of which, we venerate in their ashes." — Collect, Feast of the Holy Relics

Part I, Chapter 19: The Life Everlasting

STUDY

- life everlasting
- blessed
- reprobate
- death
- judgment
- heaven
- purgatory
- hell
- light of glory

REFLECT

- I will remember my death — *memento mori.*
- What have I done for the poor souls in purgatory lately?
- Am I sufficiently desirous of heaven (or afraid of hell)?

DISCUSS

- Have encountered any of the "main errors about the last things"?
- Have you heard of the "heroic act of charity for the poor souls" before? Why is it so important to help the souls in purgatory?
- It is always hard to imagine the happiness of heaven; is this more or less difficult in our time? Why?

LEX CREDENDI

"What is *life everlasting*? It is a life that will follow this present life, and will have no end. It is a life of eternal happiness in heaven for the just, in which they participate in the beatitude of God; or it is eternal condemnation in hell for the wicked, also called 'the second death' (Apoc 21:8)." — *Credo*, 112

LEX ORANDI

"O God, Whose property is ever to have mercy and to spare, we humbly supplicate Thee for the soul of Thy servant, N., which Thou hast this day called out of this world; deliver it not to the hands of the enemy, nor forget it forever, but command it to be received by the holy angels and taken to Paradise, its home, so that, since it hath hoped and believed in Thee, it may not bear the pains of hell, but possess everlasting joys." — Collect, Mass for the Dead

Part II, Chapter 1: Human Acts

STUDY

- natural morality
- Christian morality
- natural acts
- supernatural acts
- ignorance
- concupiscence
- moral responsibility
- object
- circumstances
- end
- conscience

REFLECT

- Do I put conscious effort into making my good actions *supernatural*?
- What issues or concepts do I need to be better informed on, for my own conscience?
- Do I take sufficient responsibility for my actions? Do I do others the honor of expecting the same from them?

DISCUSS

- Give an example of an action that lacks any one of the three essential qualities of a morally *good* act (object, circumstance, intention).
- Where do you see the various "false moral systems" today, and why are they so dangerous?
- In information-saturated societies, how can we best inform our own consciences, and those of others?

LEX CREDENDI

"What is a *supernatural* act? One that is done with the assistance of grace, such as helping a neighbor for the love of God and for love of his soul's salvation." — *Credo*, 124

LEX ORANDI

"O Almighty and eternal God, direct our actions in conformity with Thy good pleasure, that in the name of Thy beloved Son we may be worthy to abound in good works." —Collect, Sunday in the Octave of Christmas

Part II, Chapter 2: The Moral Law

STUDY

- eternal law
- natural law
- divine law
- human law
- Old Law
- conflict in laws

REFLECT

- I will meditate on divine Wisdom as the cause of all law.
- Do I have sufficient respect for all forms of law?
- What would I do in the face of an unjust law? How would I recognize it?

DISCUSS

- What examples of the natural moral law do you see observed in non-Christian nations and cultures?
- In our society, many laws could be called "acts of violence rather than true laws"; what should be done about them?
- Give an example of when an ecclesiastical law might be "manifestly harmful"; what would you do in such a situation?

LEX CREDENDI

"What is the *eternal law*? It is God Himself. 'His law is not distinct from Himself,' for God is divine Wisdom and the Order by which all things are measured and guided. This ordering of divine Wisdom directs the actions and movements of all things to their due end." — *Credo*, 127

LEX ORANDI

"May the Lord our God incline our hearts unto Himself that we may walk in all His ways: and that we may keep His commandments, and His ceremonies, and all His judgments which He commanded our fathers." —Offertory, St. Vincent de Paul

Part II, Chapter 3: Virtue

STUDY

- virtue
- theological virtue
- moral virtue
- supernatural virtue
- natural virtue
- infused virtue
- acquired virtue

REFLECT

- Would others consider me a virtuous person? Why or why not?
- Have I known someone with virtue that I consider heroic?
- What particular actions could I be performing, to grow in natural or supernatural virtue?

DISCUSS

- Some have called virtues "moral muscles"—is this a good definition? Why or why not?
- How do you recognize virtues in others?
- Give an example of how virtue can be inherently attractive, even to the non-Catholic.

"How are the theological and infused moral virtues increased? By an increase of divine grace in the soul. Whatever increases grace (e.g., sacraments, prayers, good works) also increases the infused virtues." — *Credo*, 132

"O Lord, God of virtues, Who dost restore what is ruined and preserve what is restored, increase the peoples who shall be renewed by the sanctification of Thy name, that all those who are washed in holy baptism may be continually guided by Thy inspiration." — Prayer, Vigil of Pentecost

Part II, Chapter 4: Faith

STUDY

- supernatural faith
- living faith
- dead faith
- motive of faith
- motives of credibility

- principle of fidelity to Tradition
- Modernism
- *sensus fidei*
- habitual faith

- actual faith
- sins against faith
- Freemasonry
- act of faith

REFLECT

- How strong is my faith? My *sensus fidei*?
- Do I fulfill my own obligation to "acquire a deeper understanding and faith in accord with [my] own ability and state in life"?
- Am I sufficiently aware and informed about Modernism, Freemasonry, and other contemporary enemies of the Church? Do I effectively oppose them as necessary?

DISCUSS

- What makes supernatural faith different from merely natural faith or "belief"?
- How would you respond to someone claiming that fidelity to Tradition is *not* "essential for right faith"?
- Have you encountered any of the "sins against faith" in your own experience? What did you do in response?

Lex Credendi

"Is faith a necessary virtue for salvation? Yes. 'The one who does not believe will be condemned' (Mk 16:16). Faith is an absolutely necessary condition for the reception of sanctifying grace, without which no one can be saved." — *Credo*, 135

Lex Orandi

"O God, Who willest that all men should be saved and come to the knowledge of the truth, send, we beseech Thee, laborers to Thy harvest, and give them to speak Thy word with all confidence, that Thy message may run and may be made plain, and that all peoples may know Thee, the only true God, and Him Whom Thou hast sent, Jesus Christ our Lord." — Collect, Mass for the Propagation of the Faith

Part II, Chapter 5: Hope

STUDY

- hope
- object of hope
- reasons for hope
- necessity of hope
- despair
- presumption
- act of hope

REFLECT

- How strong is my hope?
- Does the hope for heaven animate my prayer?
- Am I careful to avoid presumption, making true acts of hope?

DISCUSS

- Sinful despair is common in decadent cultures. How can we bring hope?
- What are some historical examples of maintaining supernatural hope, even in spite of grave trials?
- Share a time when you had serious need of supernatural hope.

Lex Credendi

"What is hope? Hope is a supernatural virtue by which we firmly desire and trust that God will give us eternal life and the necessary means to obtain it, because He is a loving Father who keeps His promises." — *Credo*, 142

Lex Orandi

"O God, the protector of all who hope in Thee, without Whom nothing is strong, nothing is holy, multiply Thy mercy upon us, that, with Thee for our ruler and leader, we may so pass through the good things of this life as not to lose those which are eternal." —Collect, Third Sunday after Pentecost

Part II, Chapter 6: Charity

STUDY

- charity
- love
- motives of charity
- fraternal charity
- corporal works of mercy
- spiritual works of mercy
- scandal
- cooperation in evil
- act of love

REFLECT

- How strong is my charity?
- Am I careful to set a good example, avoiding both *scandal* and *cooperation in evil*?
- Do I practice the works of mercy? Which can I put into practice now?

DISCUSS

- Why is love more than a pleasant feeling, and why is it so important to understand what true love is today?
- Why is fraternal charity increasingly at risk when God is forgotten?
- Describe a time when you practiced a work of mercy, or received mercy from another.

"What is charity? The supernatural virtue by which we love God above all things for His own sake, and our neighbor as ourselves for the love of God." — *Credo*, 144

LEX ORANDI

"May the heavenly mystery, O Lord, enkindle in us that fire of love, whereby the blessed Teresa, Thy virgin, offered herself to Thee as a victim of charity for men." —Postcommunion, St. Teresa of the Infant Jesus

Part II, Chapter 7: The Moral Virtues

STUDY

- prudence
- justice
- fortitude
- temperance
- modesty
- overindulgence
- Christian mortification

REFLECT

- Which of the moral virtues do I need to grow in?
- I will meditate on Proverbs 14:15: "The prudent man looks where he is going."
- Do I practice sufficient Christian mortification?

DISCUSS

- Intemperance seems endemic in many societies; why do you think that is?
- What makes a given appearance or behavior modest or immodest?
- Which of the four cardinal virtues is your favorite? Why?

Lex Credendi

"What is a moral virtue? Any virtue that regulates the appetites and free actions of man according to reason, ordering them to the good." — *Credo*, 149

Lex Orandi

"O God of virtues, to Whom belongeth every excellent thing, implant in our hearts the love of Thy name, and bestow upon us the increase of religion, fostering what things are good, and, by Thy loving care, guarding what Thou hast fostered." — Collect, Sixth Sunday after Pentecost

Part II, Chapter 8: Sin

STUDY

- sin
- personal sin
- Original Sin
- near occasion of sin
- mortal sin
- venial sin
- sins that cry to heaven
- sins against the Holy Spirit

REFLECT

- I will meditate on the justice of God, who will punish every sin in proper measure, either in this life or the next.
- Are there any habitual sins in my life that I need to convert from?
- Do I consciously serve God with all my thoughts, words, and actions?

DISCUSS

- How might the Lutheran and Jansenist errors about Original Sin open the door to justifying gravely immoral acts?
- What causes of sin do you find to be the most prominent today? How can these be avoided?
- Would it really "be better for the whole universe to be destroyed, than to attempt to save it by committing even one venial sin"?

LEX CREDENDI

"What is sin? Sin is any voluntary violation of the law of God in thought, word, deed, or omission; whereby we fail to do what we ought or go beyond the just limits of our moral freedom, and commit evil." —*Credo*, 153

LEX ORANDI

"From my secret sins cleanse me, O Lord; and from those of others spare Thy servant. If they shall have no dominion over me, then shall I be without spot; and I shall be cleansed from the greatest sin." —Gradual, Tuesday in the Third Week of Lent

Part II, Chapter 9: The Capital Sins

STUDY

- capital/deadly sins
- pride
- avarice
- lust
- wrath
- gluttony
- envy
- sloth
- remedies

REFLECT

- Do I love myself in a proper and ordered way?
- Do I fear God more than the opinions of others?
- Which capital sin should I be most on guard against?

DISCUSS

- Will cultures that emphasize "self-love" always tend to encourage sin? Why or why not?
- Why is human respect "especially common today"? What practical steps can be taken to lessen the fear of public opinion?
- Describe two things that surprised you in reading about the seven deadly sins.

LEX CREDENDI

"Was pride the original and most dangerous vice? Yes. It was the first sin of a rational creature, the fallen angels: 'Satan was not thrown out of heaven because of fornication or adultery or theft, but rather pride has thrown him out of heaven into the deepest depths of hell.'" — *Credo*, 158

LEX ORANDI

"Grant unto Thy Church, we beseech Thee, O Lord, by the intercession of Thy holy martyrs,… to forego the spirit of pride and progress in the humility which is pleasing to Thee, that, contemning base things, it may, with generous charity, practice all those things which are right." —Collect, Sts. Vitus, Modestus, and Crescentia

Part II, Chapter 10: Temptation

STUDY

- temptation
- world
- flesh
- devil
- suggestion
- delectation
- consent
- combatting temptation

REFLECT

- What tempts me? Why?
- Are there any situations or relationships that should be changed in my life, in order to avoid temptation?
- How can I improve my methods for combatting temptation?

_____

_____

_____

_____

DISCUSS

- Why do you think the "three sources of temptation" are seldom discussed anymore, even in Christian circles?
- How might temptation contribute to God's glory or our neighbor's salvation?
- Why is it best to simply ignore and dismiss some temptations, especially those "against faith, charity, and chastity"?

_____

_____

_____

_____

LEX CREDENDI

"How does temptation promote the glory of God? When by God's grace we overcome temptation, it manifests His power in overcoming evil, His wisdom in arranging a way for us to escape evil, and His goodness in giving us grace to overcome evil." — *Credo*, 165

LEX ORANDI

"O God, Who on this day didst remove blessed Henry, Thy confessor, from the crown of an earthly empire to an everlasting kingdom, we humbly beseech Thee that, as, protected by the abundance of Thy grace, Thou didst enable him to overcome the temptations of the world, so Thou make us, in imitation of him, to avoid the allurements of this world and to come with pure minds unto Thee." —Collect, St. Henry, Emperor

Part II, Chapter 11:
Commandments in General

STUDY

- the Decalogue
- the two great commandments
- the six precepts of the Church

REFLECT

- I will meditate on God's revelation of the Commandments on Mount Sinai.
- Which of the commandments do I excel at following? How can I inspire others to the same?
- Which of the precepts of the Church do I find the most difficult? Why?

DISCUSS

- Which of the Ten Commandments do you think is most necessary to preach about today, and why?
- Is it easier to love God or neighbor? Why?
- Why is it so essential to maintain the love of God as the "first and greatest commandment"?

LEX CREDENDI

"Did God limit Himself to merely declaring His law? No; He also engraved it on two tablets of stone, which He delivered to Moses; and with the coming of the Son of God to earth, He promulgated it anew and perfected it, by bestowing the grace that enables man to follow God's law in righteousness." — *Credo*, 166

LEX ORANDI

"I will meditate on Thy commandments, which I have loved exceedingly: and lift up my hand to Thy commandments, which I have loved." —Offertory, Ember Wednesday in September

Part II, Chapter 12: First Commandment

STUDY

- right worship
- Christian worship
- *latria*
- *dulia*
- *hyperdulia*
- principal acts of worship
- saints
- relics
- images
- superstition
- irreligion

REFLECT

- Is my worship of God sufficiently *internal* and *external*?
- Do I have sufficient devotion to the angels and saints?
- Is anyone in my life engaged in sins against right worship? What should I do?

DISCUSS

- Do most people think of sins against right worship as being infinitely worse than murder? Why or why not?
- Describe a time when you had to avoid a situation of superstition or irreligion.
- Share about your favorite saint to pray to, or a particular relic or image that especially aids your devotion.

Lex Credendi

"Are sins of superstition very grave? Yes. They are among the most serious sins that man can commit, because right worship of the true God is man's highest moral obligation. 'True worshippers will worship the Father in spirit and truth, for the Father seeks such as these to worship Him. God is spirit, and those who worship Him must worship in spirit and truth' (Jn 4:23–24)." — *Credo*, 172

Lex Orandi

"Let us pray, also, for the pagans, that Almighty God may remove iniquity from their hearts, so that they may leave their idols and be converted to the living and true God and His only Son, Jesus Christ, our Lord and God." —Supplication for Pagans, Good Friday

Part II, Chapter 13: Second Commandment

STUDY

- blasphemy
- oaths
- indiscreet vows
- breaking of vows
- Oath against Modernism
- obligation of vows

REFLECT

- Do I have sufficient respect for God's name?
- Have I taken a solemn oath or vow? Have I kept it?
- How would I react if someone took God's name in vain in my presence?

DISCUSS

- Blasphemy has become widespread, even in once-Christian nations. How can we reverse this trend?
- Look up and discuss the Oath against Modernism—is it still "very useful and timely" today? Why or why not?
- In many countries, perjury is no longer considered an especially grave crime in civil law. Why do you think this is?

"What does the second commandment forbid? It forbids us to profane God's holy name by careless use of it, blasphemy, false or unjust oaths, indiscreet vows, and the breaking of vows." — *Credo*, 174

Lex Orandi

"O God, Who didst appoint Thine only-begotten Son to be the Savior of the human race, and didst command that He be called Jesus, mercifully grant that we may enjoy in heaven the vision of Him Whose holy name we venerate on earth." —Collect, Most Holy Name of Jesus

Part II, Chapter 14: Third Commandment

STUDY

- Sabbath
- *Dominica*
- eighth day

- servile work
- required worship
- active participation

- suspended obligation

REFLECT

- I will meditate on the completion of Creation, when "God rested."
- Do I always attend Mass on Sundays and holy days, as I should?
- How can I deepen my interior participation at Mass?

DISCUSS

- Would a visitor to your home, city, or country notice any difference between Sunday and the other days of the week? Why or why not?
- How can we work to restore the sanctity of Sunday in our own sphere of influence?
- Describe a time when you or someone you know had legitimate reason not to attend Sunday Mass; what other means were used to sanctify Sunday?

"What day was reserved for God under the Old Law? Saturday or the *Sabbath*, a word signifying repose: 'On the seventh day God finished the work that He had done, and He rested' (Gn 2:2). What day is reserved for God under the New Law? The first day of the week, Sunday, is 'the Lord's day'—in Latin *Dominica*, as Sunday was called from apostolic times." — *Credo*, 176

LEX ORANDI

"But, in the evening of the Sabbath, when it began to dawn, toward the first day of the week, came Mary Magdalen, and the other Mary, to see the sepulcher. Alleluia." — Magnificat Antiphon, Holy Saturday

Part II, Chapter 15: Fourth Commandment

STUDY

- honor
- whom to honor
- duties in the family
- media
- obedience
- Christian education
- universal moral code
- correcting superiors

REFLECT

- Do I honor my parents? Do I respect my other superiors?
- Am I an exemplary model of virtue and holiness to my children, employees, or others I have authority over?
- Which of my duties in Church or state do I find the most challenging?

DISCUSS

- Why must all legitimate authority come from God, rather than mere force or the consent of man?
- What are some particular difficulties faced by parents today, in carrying out their own particular duties in the family?
- Describe a time in history or your own life when an inferior was compelled to justly correct a superior. What did you learn?

Lex Credendi

"What does *honor* mean, with regard to children and parents? This word embraces all duties of *filial piety*: love, respect, obedience, and assistance." — *Credo*, 180

Lex Orandi

"O Lord Jesus Christ, Who, in the days of Thy subjection to Mary and Joseph, didst consecrate home life by ineffable acts of virtue; by the intercession of Thy holy Mother and of Thy foster father, make us so to profit by the example they with Thee have set us, that we may be counted members of Thy household for evermore." — Collect, Sunday in the Octave of Epiphany

Part II, Chapter 16: Fifth Commandment

STUDY

- homicide
- suicide
- abortion
- euthanasia

- illicit medical
  products
- sterilization
- mutilation

- death penalty
- legitimate defense

REFLECT

- I will meditate on the great gift of human life.
- Have I been complicit in any sins against the Fifth Commandment? If so, have I repented and made sufficient reparation?
- Life is increasingly devalued in many societies—should I be doing more to reverse this trend?

DISCUSS

- Why, in principle, will it always be morally legitimate to kill in certain circumstances?
- Describe some of the common justifications for sins against the Fifth Commandment. What basic principle can answer them all?
- Where is there a "conspiracy against life" in our culture? How may we work to effectively oppose it?

"What acts of bodily murder are forbidden by this commandment? Homicide, suicide, abortion, and euthanasia. In addition, acts of unjust violence to bodily health or integrity, including sterilization and mutilation, and any acts of wrath or dissension that lead to murder." — *Credo*, 186

LEX ORANDI

"He that loveth not, abideth in death. Whosoever hateth his brother is a murderer: and you know that no murderer hath eternal life abiding in himself." —Epistle, Sunday in the Octave of Corpus Christi

Part II, Chapter 17: Sixth and Ninth Commandments

STUDY

- chastity
- conjugal chastity
- chastity of widowhood
- virginal chastity
- fidelity
- exterior sins against chastity
- interior sins against chastity
- maintaining chastity

REFLECT

- I will meditate on the chastity of the Son of God, Jesus Christ.
- Am I sufficiently on guard against external occasions of lust?
- Do I "read and ponder holy things" enough?

DISCUSS

- Exterior sins against chastity are increasingly widespread today—why? What can be done to combat this spread?
- Why is it so important for the Church to maintain her discipline of denying Communion to public sinners?
- Which forms of prayer are most effective for maintaining chastity? Why?

"What is chastity? The moral virtue which leads us to abstain from disordered desire for sexual pleasure or disordered use of the sexual faculties. 'Nothing is beautiful but what is pure, and the purity of men is chastity. Chastity is called honesty and the possession of it honor. It is also called integrity and its opposite corruption. In short, it has its peculiar glory of being the fair, unspotted virtue of both soul and body.'" — *Credo*, 192

Lex Orandi

"For this is the will of God, your sanctification; that you should abstain from fornication, that every one of you should know how to possess his vessel in sanctification and honor; not in the passion of lust, like the Gentiles that know not God." — Epistle, Second Sunday of Lent

Part II, Chapter 18: Seventh and Tenth Commandments

STUDY

- property
- socialism
- subsidiarity
- theft
- unjust retention
- unjust damage
- restitution
- covetousness

REFLECT

- Have I made sufficient restitution for any past sins of theft?
- Am I respectful of other people's property?
- Do I covet anything? Am I jealous of anyone?

DISCUSS

- Why are efforts to dissolve "privacy, property rights, the natural family, physical currencies, and personal ownership of the means of production" all good indicators of socialist ideologies?
- What makes socialism and other "emerging geopolitical movements" evil in themselves?
- Do you think personal communications technology has multiplied occasions of covetousness and jealousy? Why or why not?

Lex Credendi

"What does the seventh commandment require? It forbids us from unjustly taking the property of others, and obliges us to repair any harm we have done. What does the tenth commandment require? It forbids us from harboring jealousy at the goods of our neighbor, and all unjust interior desire for the property of others." — *Credo*, 196

Lex Orandi

"He that stole, let him now steal no more; but rather let him labor, working with his hands the thing which is good, that he may have something to give to him that suffereth need." —Epistle, Nineteenth Sunday after Pentecost

Part II, Chapter 19: Eighth Commandment

STUDY

- lying
- mental reservation
- equivocation
- perjury
- false testimony
- reputation

REFLECT

- Lying makes someone a liar. Am I a liar?
- Would I value the truthfulness of my words, even at the cost of my life?
- Do I have sufficient respect for my own reputation? Those of others?

DISCUSS

- Where do you see sins against the truth in wider society?
- How has the "information age" affected the very notion of one's reputation? How can reputation be formed? How is it destroyed?
- Describe a situation when it might be prudent to make a wide mental reservation.

Lex Credendi

"Is every kind of lie forbidden? Yes, because every lie violates the natural purpose of speech. They are the offspring of Satan, 'the father of lies' (Jn 8:44), offensive to Christ, who is 'the truth' (Jn 14:6), and contrary to the divine 'Spirit of truth' (Jn 14:17)." — *Credo*, 200

Lex Orandi

"These follow the Lamb whithersoever He goeth. These were purchased from among men, the firstfruits to God and to the Lamb; and in their mouth there was found no lie; for they are without spot before the throne of God." —Lesson, The Holy Innocents

Part II, Chapter 20: First Precept of the Church

STUDY

• assisting at Mass

• holy day of obligation

REFLECT

- Do I assist at Mass when I must?
- Could I attend Mass more frequently than I currently do?
- What other practices might I undertake to sanctify holy days?

DISCUSS

- Would a non-Catholic visitor to your local Catholic Church leave there with the impression that Mass is "the greatest act of worship" on earth? Why or why not?
- Why is community worship so essential, even in our individualistic age?
- What is your favorite holy day? Why?

"Is assisting at Mass the greatest act of worship? Yes. There is no religious act more agreeable to God and no prayer more efficacious, for it is the divine sacrifice and prayer of Jesus Christ together with the Church, His Bride and Mystical Body." — *Credo*, 202

Lex Orandi

"O God, Who, through the august communication of this sacrifice, dost make us partakers of the one supreme divinity, grant, we beseech Thee, that, as we know Thy truth, so we may ever follow it with worthy actions." —Secret, Eighteenth Sunday after Pentecost

Part II, Chapter 21: Second Precept of the Church

STUDY

- fasting
- abstinence

- Lent
- spirit of penance

REFLECT

- Do I at least fast and abstain when obliged to?
- Did my last Lent bear spiritual fruit in my life? How will my next Lent be even better?
- Given the benefits of fasting and abstinence, should I undertake more than I do now?

DISCUSS

- Should the Church's current law of fasting and abstinence be more strict? Why or why not?
- Why is Lent, and especially Ash Wednesday, an excellent time to give outward witness to the Faith?
- Why are self-denial and self-discipline in any form so necessary and praiseworthy in the Christian life?

LEX CREDENDI

"Are fasting and abstinence very beneficial for the soul? Yes, as they: 1. Expiate sin and appease God's justice; 2. Subdue unruly passions and keep us from sin; 3. Elevate the heart to God and supernatural realities; 4. Merit special graces; 5. Strengthen us to persevere in doing good; 6. Detach us from worldly things and inflame our love for heavenly things." — *Credo*, 205

LEX ORANDI

"O God, Who hast commanded that our bodies should be chastened by the devotion of fasting for the healing of our souls, propitiously grant us to be ever devout toward Thee both in mind and in body." —Collect, Saturday in the Octave of Pentecost

Part II, Chapter 22: Third and Fourth Precepts of the Church

STUDY

- yearly confession
- Easter Communion
- age of discretion
- Communion for infants

REFLECT

- I will meditate on the great gifts of my first sacramental confession and First Communion.
- Do I attend sacramental confession and receive Holy Communion at least annually?
- Should I frequent these sacraments more often?

DISCUSS

- Do you remember your First Communion or sacramental confession? If so, describe your experience.
- Why is it desirable that Catholics confess and receive Communion more than just annually?
- Why do you think the ancient practices of baptism and Communion for infants are sometimes opposed?

LEX CREDENDI

"What does the fourth precept of the Church require of us? It orders all the faithful with the use of reason to receive Holy Communion at least once a year, at Easter time. Is this precept also a matter of divine law? Yes. Our Lord has ordered us to receive the Blessed Sacrament: 'Unless you eat the flesh of the Son of Man and drink His blood, you have no life in you' (Jn 6:53)." — *Credo*, 206

LEX ORANDI

"Therefore, whosoever shall eat this bread, or drink the chalice of the Lord unworthily, shall be guilty of the body and of the blood of the Lord. But let a man prove himself; and so let him eat of that bread, and drink of the chalice. For he that eateth and drinketh unworthily, eateth and drinketh judgment to himself; not discerning the body of the Lord." — Epistle, Maundy Thursday

Part II, Chapter 23: Fifth and Sixth Precepts of the Church

STUDY

- pastors
- support of pastors
- marriage
- civil marriage

REFLECT

- Do I sufficiently support my pastors, and follow the Church's marriage laws?
- Have I ever witnessed heroic examples of these precepts lived out?
- What could I be doing now to instill greater respect for the Church's marriage law?

DISCUSS

- Share practical ways to support the Church's pastors.
- How would you respond if you were invited to a marriage you knew to be invalid?
- Why is it especially important today to emphasize how "marriage affects the common good"?

Lex Credendi

"What does the fifth precept of the Church require of us? It orders us to support our pastors in proportion to their needs and our means, and to contribute to the work of the Church on earth…. In funding the necessities of public worship, the care and preservation of ecclesiastical buildings, the building and equipping of schools, the support of works of charity, etc." — *Credo*, 207

_____

_____

_____

_____

_____

_____

_____

_____

_____

_____

Lex Orandi

"Carry neither purse, nor scrip, nor shoes; and salute no man by the way. Into whatsoever house you enter, first say, Peace be to this house: and if the son of peace be there, your peace shall rest upon him: but if not, it shall return to you. And in the same house remain, eating and drinking such things as they have: for the laborer is worthy of his hire." — Gospel, St. Mark the Evangelist

Part II, Chapter 24: Evangelical Counsels

STUDY

- evangelical counsels
- voluntary poverty
- supernatural charity
- perpetual chastity
- perfect obedience
- religious life
- cloistered life

REFLECT

- Do I pray for those in consecrated life, or ask them to pray for me?
- How am I using my own personal wealth for the glory of God and sanctification of souls?
- Have I ever considered entering religious life, or encouraged another to do so?

DISCUSS

- Why is it important to recall that material wealth is neither good nor evil in itself?
- Describe a time when a consecrated religious person made a positive impact on your life.
- What is your favorite religious order, and why? Have you ever visited a religious house? What was it like?

"What is an *evangelical counsel*? Some means of attaining perfection in holiness, which we find recommended in the Gospel." — *Credo*, 209

_____

_____

_____

_____

_____

_____

_____

_____

_____

_____

_____

_____

_____

_____

_____

_____

_____

_____

LEX ORANDI

"Jesus looking on him, loved him, and said to him: One thing is wanting unto thee: go, sell whatsoever thou hast, and give to the poor, and thou shalt have treasure in heaven; and come, follow Me." —Gospel, St. Gabriel of Our Lady of Sorrows

Part II, Chapter 25: The Beatitudes

STUDY

- beatitude in itself
- evangelical Beatitudes
- rewards of the Beatitudes

REFLECT

- Do I truly desire *beatitude*? Could an outside observer tell this about me?
- Which of the eight Beatitudes most appeals to me? Why?
- Which of the Beatitudes do I find the most challenging? Why?

DISCUSS

- Share a time when you saw any of the Beatitudes lived out in a remarkable way.
- Which Beatitude is most sorely needed in our society today? Why?
- Why is the eighth Beatitude a kind of "summary" of all the others?

Lex Credendi

"What is true meekness? It consists in mastery of our passions and acting toward our neighbor with charity and humility, without sharpness, disdain, or impatience. What is *the land* promised to the meek? 1. The land of our own hearts, of which we are always masters; 2. The land of others' hearts, which we conquer by amiability; 3. The land of the blessed, i.e., heaven." — *Credo*, 214

Lex Orandi

"O God, Who didst vouchsafe to confer on St. Rita such great grace that she loved her enemies and bore in her heart and on her brow the stigmata of Thy love and Passion, grant us, we beseech Thee, by her intercession and merits, so to spare our enemies and to meditate on the pains of Thy Passion that we may obtain the rewards promised to the meek and to them that mourn." —Collect, St. Rita

Part III, Chapter 1: Grace

STUDY

- grace
- naturalism
- actual grace
- charismatic gifts
- sanctifying grace
- state of grace
- effects of grace

REFLECT

- I will ask God for a greater measure of efficacious grace.
- How can I be growing "in the grace and knowledge of Our Lord and Savior Jesus Christ"?
- Do I regard sanctifying grace as my most precious treasure?

DISCUSS

- Where do you find the two general errors about divine grace in our society today?
- Have you ever encountered someone that you thought was "faithful to grace from moment to moment"?
- Why would it be a failure in charity to act as though sanctifying grace were already present in every soul?

"We can do nothing in the supernatural order without actual grace; that is, nothing in the way of our eternal salvation.... God always takes the initiative in our sanctification. By actual grace, God moves a person who is in a state of sin to perform acts, such as prayer, that can lead to *saving faith*: that grace which enables us to begin to believe, and then accompanies and follows us so that we may persevere in faith and holiness to the end of our life." — *Credo*, 220

_____

_____

_____

_____

_____

_____

_____

_____

_____

_____

_____

_____

LEX ORANDI

"O God, the strength of them that hope in Thee, graciously be present with us when we invoke Thee, and, because mortal infirmity can do nothing without Thee, grant us the assistance of Thy grace that, in executing Thy commands, we may be pleasing to Thee both in our desires and in our deeds." — Collect, Trinity Sunday

Part III, Chapter 2: Justification and Merit

STUDY

- justification
- loss of justification
- restoration of

justification
- merit
- natural merit

- supernatural merit
- source of merit

REFLECT

- Do I understand myself as truly a "new creature" by grace?
- Are there signs in my own life that give me hope of justification?
- Am I striving to merit grace today?

DISCUSS

- How can we work for greater merit, while not attributing it entirely to ourselves?
- Why is it so critical to hold that justification may be lost by our sin, but never taken from us without our consent?
- Describe a time when you experienced God's grace as truly "a greater miracle than the raising of the dead to life."

Lex Credendi

"How have the saints regarded their own merits? 'They do not glory in their own merits, for they attribute no good to themselves but all to Me, because out of My infinite charity I gave all to them.' As St. Thérèse of Lisieux maintains: 'In the evening of this life, I shall appear before You with empty hands, for I do not ask You, Lord, to count my works. All our justice is blemished in Your eyes. I wish, then, to be clothed in Your own justice and to receive from Your love the eternal possession of Yourself.'" — *Credo*, 224

Lex Orandi

"Give ear, O Lord, to our supplication, that we who put no trust in our own justice may be helped by the merits of those who have been pleasing to Thee." —Secret, Sts. Faustinus and Jovita

Part III, Chapter 3: Prayer in General

STUDY

- prayer
- growth in prayer
- necessity of prayer
- circumstances of prayer

REFLECT

- Do I pray daily, and well?
- How might I grow in the grace of prayer this year?
- For whom should I be praying in a special way?

DISCUSS

- Practically speaking, how can we "pray without ceasing" in our busy lives?
- Tell about a saint that models the life of prayer in a special way for you, or to whom you especially like to pray.
- Describe how you take time for focused prayer in your own daily life.

"'We ought always to pray' (Lk 18:1), and 'pray without ceasing' (1 Thes 5:17).... because we are: 1. God's creatures by nature, who acknowledge His supreme authority by prayer; 2. His children by grace, who thank Him and seek His blessing by prayer; 3. His 'fellow workers,' the willing instruments of His work in the world (see 1 Cor 3:9), made effective by prayer." — *Credo*, 226

LEX ORANDI

"O God, Who didst adorn blessed Francis, as the founder of a new order, with the spirit of prayer and the love of penance, grant Thy servants to make such progress in imitating him that, by prayer without ceasing, and by bringing the body into subjection, they may deserve to attain heavenly glory." — Collect, St. Francis Caracciolo

Part III, Chapter 4: Life of Prayer

STUDY

- qualities of prayer
- adoration
- thanksgiving
- atonement
- petition
- intercession
- vocal prayer
- mental prayer
- meditation
- contemplation
- effects of prayer

REFLECT

- In my prayer, do I "seek first His Kingdom"? Why or why not?
- I will resolve to take more time for mental prayer this year.
- When I promise to pray for someone, do I really do so?

DISCUSS

- What form(s) of prayer do you find most edifying?
- Have you ever experienced dryness in prayer? If so, what helped you through it?
- Describe a time when prayer helped you or someone you know through a very difficult situation.

LEX CREDENDI

"What is meant by praying *in the name* of Jesus Christ? Praying to God *through* Christ, *with* Christ, and *in* Christ: 1. Relying solely on His merits; 2. Uniting ourselves to His prayer and sacrifice; 3. Asking those blessings that He has merited for us; 4. Being deeply convinced that He Himself prays within us." — *Credo*, 228

LEX ORANDI

"Be at hand, O Lord, we beseech Thee, before our actions with the movements of Thy grace and in their doing follow them with Thy help, that every prayer and wish of ours may begin in Thee, and begun in Thee, through Thee we may finish them." —Prayer after the Fourth Gradual, Ember Saturday in Lent

Part III, Chapter 5: Principal Prayers

STUDY

- Pater Noster
- Ave Maria
- Gloria Patri

REFLECT

- Do I say the three principal prayers every day? Why or why not?
- When I pray, do I truly regard God as my loving Father?
- Do all my actions give praise to the Holy Trinity, as in the Gloria Patri?

DISCUSS

- What is your favorite line of the Pater Noster? Why?
- How would you answer the common accusation that Catholics "worship" Mary in the Ave Maria?
- The Gloria Patri in Latin is among the oldest Christian prayers; can you recite it by heart?

LEX CREDENDI

"Why do Christians say *our* Father, and not *my* Father? To remind us that we: 1. Are brethren by being incorporated into Jesus Christ; 2. Ought to live in peace and unity; 3. Should pray for one another, as St. Cyprian explained: 'The Teacher of peace and the Master of unity would not have prayer to be made singly and individually, . . . and when we pray, we pray not for one, but for the whole people, because we, the whole people, are one.'" — *Credo*, 232

LEX ORANDI

"Admonished by salutary precepts, and following divine directions, we presume to say: Our Father, Who art in heaven, hallowed be Thy name; Thy kingdom come; Thy will be done on earth as it is in heaven; give us this day our daily bread; and forgive us our trespasses, as we forgive those who trespass against us, and lead us not into temptation. But deliver us from evil. Amen." — Pater Noster, Ordinary of Mass

Part III, Chapter 6: Sacraments in General

STUDY

- sacrament
- number of sacraments
- divisions of sacraments
- matter
- form
- minister
- intention
- necessary dispositions
- sacramental character
- ceremonies

REFLECT

- I will thank God for the amazing gift of the seven sacraments.
- Have I committed the definition of *sacrament* to memory?
- Am I always sure to be well-disposed when receiving any sacrament?

DISCUSS

- Have you ever thought of the sacraments as "unique divine inventions"? Which one strikes you as the most brilliant, and why?
- Describe a time when you encountered one of the "errors about the sacraments."
- Catholics are sometimes accused of believing in "magic" with regard to the sacraments. How would you respond?

LEX CREDENDI

"How do the sacraments produce grace? Each sacrament is a unique divine invention, producing grace in the soul according to each sacrament's intended purpose, provided that the recipient poses no obstacle to it." — *Credo*, 238

LEX ORANDI

"May the working of Thy power, we beg Thee, O Lord, be increased in us, that, being nourished by divine sacraments, we may by Thy grace be prepared to obtain that which they promise." — Postcommunion, Ordinary of Mass

Part III, Chapter 7: Baptism

STUDY

- baptism
- infusion
- immersion
- aspersion
- essential form
- infant baptism
- "baptism of desire"
- "baptism of blood"
- baptism in cases of necessity
- effects of baptism
- baptismal vows
- destiny of the non-baptized

REFLECT

- I will thank God for my own baptism, and resolve to renew my baptismal promises at least annually.
- Do I have a positive, faith-building relationship with my own baptismal sponsor(s) today? Why or why not?
- I will resolve to be more intentional about assisting any soul(s) for whom I am in some way responsible, especially if I am a godparent.

DISCUSS

- Describe your own or someone else's baptism that you attended.
- Have you ever needed to administer an emergency baptism, or do you know someone who has? Explain.
- Do you renew your baptismal promises every year? Why or why not?

Lex Credendi

"What are the effects of baptism? 1. It gives sanctifying grace, which regenerates us in Christ Jesus; 2. It gives a new birth in the Holy Spirit, making us adopted children of God the Father; 3. It makes us members of the Church; 4. It washes away all sin; 5. It imparts a sacramental character, indelibly imprinted on the soul." — *Credo*, 245

Lex Orandi

"Here may the stains of all sins be washed away: here may nature, created to Thine image, and reformed to the honorable estate of its origin, be cleansed of all the foulness of the past, that every human being, by entering into this sacrament of regeneration, may be born again into a new infancy of true innocence." — Prayer for Withdrawing the Paschal Candle, Holy Saturday

Part III, Chapter 8: Confirmation

STUDY

- confirmation
- dispositions for adult confirmation
- effects of confirmation
- personal holiness
- Pentecostalism

REFLECT

- I will thank God for the great gift of confirmation.
- Which of the gifts, fruits, or other graces of the Holy Spirit am I most in need of right now?
- Have I had occasion to "confess Jesus Christ by word and deed"?

DISCUSS

- Describe your experience of your own confirmation, or another's that you attended.
- Whom do you see actively living out the graces of their confirmation?
- Growth in holiness is an obligation on every Christian; how will this contribute to "authentic renewal" in the Church? In the world? Is personal growth in holiness enough?

Lex Credendi

"Why does confirmation bring more abundant gifts of the Holy Spirit? Because confirmation is a kind of sacramental extension of Pentecost, whereby the Holy Spirit more richly empowers the faithful to undertake the spiritual combat and external witness of the Christian life." — *Credo*, 252

Lex Orandi

"Alleluia, alleluia. Send forth Thy Spirit, and they shall be created: and Thou shalt renew the face of the earth. Alleluia. Come, O Holy Spirit, fill the hearts of Thy faithful: and kindle in them the fire of Thy love." —Greater Alleluia, Pentecost

Part III, Chapter 9.1: Eucharist as Sacrament

STUDY

- Eucharist
- consecration
- Real Presence
- transubstantiation
- administration
- dispositions of soul and body
- Communion in the hand
- kinds of communion
- effects of the Eucharist
- duties to the Eucharist

REFLECT

- I will meditate on Christ's institution of the Eucharist during the Last Supper.
- When was the last time I worshipped Our Lord in the Eucharist? When will the next time be?
- Do I take particular care to be well disposed before receiving the tremendous gift of Our Lord in Holy Communion?

DISCUSS

- Describe a time when you took part in Eucharistic worship outside of Holy Mass; Corpus Christi procession, Eucharistic congress, Forty Hours devotion, etc.
- Have you ever encountered any of the "principal errors about the dogma of Christ's Real Presence in the Eucharist," or the "spiritually harmful" practice of Communion in the hand? How did you respond?
- Should the bodily fast before receiving Holy Communion be more strict than it currently is? Why or why not?

LEX CREDENDI

"What is the *Eucharist*? The sacrament that perpetuates the sacrifice of the Cross, in which Christ's immolated and glorified body and blood are really, truly, and substantially offered, present, contained, and received under the appearances of bread and wine." — *Credo*, 255

LEX ORANDI

"O God, Who in this wonderful sacrament hast left us a memorial of Thy Passion, grant us, we beseech Thee, so to venerate the sacred mysteries of Thy body and blood that we may constantly experience in ourselves the fruit of Thy Redemption." — Collect, Corpus Christi

Part III, Chapter 9.2: Eucharist as Sacrifice

STUDY

- sacrifice
- immolation
- oblation
- sacrifice of Calvary
- Sacrifice of the Mass
- eternal priesthood
- heavenly liturgy
- offering Mass
- assisting at Mass

REFLECT

- I will meditate on the sacrifice of Calvary, made present at every Holy Mass.
- Do I understand the definition of *sacrifice*?
- Am I practicing the best means for assisting at Mass?

DISCUSS

- Do you see any of the "major errors about the Sacrifice of the Mass" as being prevalent in our own time?
- Would it be fair to say that Holy Mass is not principally "for us," but rather, "for God"? Why or why not?
- Describe a particularly memorable Holy Mass that you attended in the past.

"What is the Sacrifice of the Mass? It is the very sacrifice of the Cross, now really and truly re-presented and offered to God in an unbloody manner, under the external appearances of bread and wine." — *Credo*, 268

"Grant us, we beseech Thee, O Lord, worthily to frequent these mysteries, for as often as the commemoration of this victim is celebrated, the work of our Redemption is performed." — Secret, Ninth Sunday after Pentecost

Part III, Chapter 10: Penance

STUDY

- virtue of penance
- sacrament of penance
- absolution
- seal of confession
- administration of penance
- effects of penance
- acts of the penitent (contrition, confession, satisfaction)
- suffrages
- indulgences

REFLECT

- I will meditate on the forgiveness of God, and Christ's institution of the sacrament of penance.
- How long has it been since my last confession? When will I go next?
- Do I always perform my sacramental penance with promptness? What additional penance could I (or should I) undertake to make reparation for the sins of my past, or those of others?

DISCUSS

- Share any stories that you may know where a priest had to maintain the seal of confession despite external pressure. Why is such secrecy so important?
- Some think of penance as "a counseling session," as if the priest were a psychotherapist; why is it important to instead view the priest as a true judge and physician of souls in this sacrament?
- When was the last time you gained an indulgence? When will you gain one next? Do you have a favorite?

LEX CREDENDI

"Is penance a necessary virtue? Yes. God can only forgive the repentant: 'Repent and turn from all your transgressions, lest iniquity be your ruin' (Ez 18:30); for, 'unless you repent you will all likewise perish' (Lk 13:5)." — *Credo*, 273

LEX ORANDI

"O God, Who art moved by humiliation and appeased by penance, incline the ear of Thy goodness to our prayers, and when the heads of Thy servants are touched with these ashes, graciously pour forth the grace of Thy blessing, that Thou mayest fill them with the spirit of compunction and mayest effectually grant what they righteously ask, and ordain that what Thou grantest may remain forever established and unmoved." — Blessing of the Ashes, Ash Wednesday

Part III, Chapter 11: Anointing of the Sick or Extreme Unction

STUDY

- anointing of the sick
- extreme unction
- effects
- administration of anointing of the sick
- last rites
- dispositions for this sacrament

REFLECT

- I will meditate on the hour of my death, and ask God that I may have the last rites available to me when that time comes.
- Do I have in my residence any items that a priest might need in administering anointing of the sick?
- Have any of my departed friends or loved ones received anointing of the sick? Do I still pray for their souls?

DISCUSS

- Why is it important to highlight the spiritual effects of anointing of the sick over its potential physical benefits?
- Have you ever witnessed anointing of the sick? Describe the experience.
- Some clinicians advocate for drug-induced unconsciousness as death approaches, even when serious pain is not present. Might such a practice interfere with the graces of anointing of the sick, or be a disservice to the dying Christian? Why or why not?

"What are the effects of this sacrament?… This sacrament: 1. Confers sanctifying grace; 2. Remits sin; 3. Effaces all remains of sin; 4. Consoles and strengthens the soul, especially for its final struggle and judgment.… This sacrament can relieve the sufferings of the sick person, and may even restore bodily health if God judges this advantageous to his soul." — *Credo*, 287

Lex Orandi

"Is any man sick among you? Let him bring in the priests of the Church, and let them pray over him, anointing him with oil in the name of the Lord. And the prayer of faith shall save the sick man: and the Lord shall raise him up: and if he be in sins, they shall be forgiven him." — Epistle, Mass for the Sick

Part III, Chapter 12: Holy Orders

STUDY

- holy orders
- common priesthood
- ministerial priesthood
- major orders
- minor orders
- priestly celibacy
- *munera* of the priesthood
- power of order
- power of jurisdiction
- impediments to holy orders
- effects of holy orders
- women's ordination

REFLECT

- I will thank God for the great gift of holy orders, and ask Him to send more holy priests and bishops into the vineyard of His Church.
- Have I ever considered a vocation to the priesthood, or encouraged the same in another?
- How do I regard the pastors of the Church in my area? How can I support their good work?

DISCUSS

- Describe a time when a man in holy orders had a positive impact on your life.
- In our day, some are led to regard priests as mere "event managers" or "emcees" in the local church. What leads to this attitude? Why is it an injustice to the priesthood?
- Clerical celibacy and "women's ordination" have been increasingly contested since the mid-twentieth century. Why do you think this is? How would you approach these topics with someone in conversation?

LEX CREDENDI

"What is *holy orders*? A sacrament instituted by Christ that permanently changes the soul of a man to make him participate in Our Lord's divine priesthood, giving spiritual power and grace to discharge sacred duties worthily." — *Credo*, 288

LEX ORANDI

"O God, Who unto the glory of Thy majesty and the salvation of the human race hast ordained Thy only-begotten Son a Priest Most High and Eternal: grant that those ministers and dispensers of His mysteries whom He hath chosen may be found faithful in fulfilling the ministry which they have accepted." —Collect, Votive Mass of Jesus Christ the High Priest

Part III, Chapter 13: Marriage

STUDY

- marriage
- sacramental marriage
- unity
- indissolubility
- exclusivity
- end of marriage
- threefold good
- administration of marriage
- nuptial Mass
- marriage impediments
- marriage banns
- effects and duties of marriage
- domestic church
- large families

REFLECT

- I will thank God for the institution of marriage, and its elevation to the level of a sacrament.
- If I am married, am I fulfilling my duties well? If not, am I preparing well, or supporting others who are?
- Am I doing enough to combat the various "errors about marriage" in civil society?

DISCUSS

- Describe a time when a married person or couple had a positive impact on your life.
- Share anything that especially encouraged or surprised you in this chapter.
- With so many "errors about marriage" in contemporary society, how might we be greater witnesses to God's truth about marriage and family?

LEX CREDENDI

"Who instituted the sacrament of marriage? God Himself first instituted marriage in the Garden of Eden, and the Incarnate Son of God, Jesus Christ, then raised it to the dignity of a sacrament.... In His perfect wisdom, God created marriage to secure peace and union within families, safety and provision for children, and stability in human society, as well as to serve as a mystical sign of His own unfailing love for the Church." — *Credo*, 299–300

LEX ORANDI

"O God, Who... didst bestow on man, whom Thou hadst created in Thine own likeness, the inseparable help of woman, fashioning her body from his very flesh, and thereby teaching us that it is never lawful to put asunder what it has pleased Thee to make of one substance; O God, Who hast consecrated wedlock by a surpassing mystery, since in the marriage bond Thou didst foreshow the union of Christ with the Church.... Look down in mercy." — Prayer, Nuptial Mass

Part III, Chapter 14: Sacramentals

STUDY

- sacramentals
- invocative blessings
- constitutive blessings
- sacramental objects

REFLECT

- I will thank God for the great gift of sacramentals.
- Do I make regular use of sacramentals? Which one is my favorite?
- Sacramentals make excellent gifts, especially on holy occasions. Have I ever given the gift of a sacramental to someone else? Why or why not?

DISCUSS

- Describe a time when you have used a sacramental to noticeably good effect.
- What is your favorite sacramental? Why?
- Have you ever seen films or read books including the Church's solemn rite of exorcism? Did you think it was a fair portrayal of this sacramental? Why or why not?

LEX CREDENDI

"What are the effects of the sacramentals? They vary, depending on each sacramental. By the prayer of the Church, they may: 1. Obtain actual graces; 2. Remit venial sins for which we repent; 3. Remit the temporal punishment due to sins already forgiven; 4. Drive out demons; 5. Cure or relieve sickness; 5. End disasters, famine, disease, and war; 6. Improve the fertility of farms, efficiency of tools, etc." — *Credo*, 311

LEX ORANDI

"O God... bless these branches of palm and of olive which Thy servants take up in the spirit of faith, that, into whatsoever place they shall be brought, the dwellers in that place may obtain Thy blessing, and that, putting to flight all evil, Thy right hand may protect those who have been redeemed by Jesus Christ, Thy Son, our Lord." —Blessing of Palms, Palm Sunday

Part III, Chapter 15: Sacred Liturgy

STUDY

- liturgy
- rubrics
- *lex orandi, lex credendi*
- origin of liturgy
- traditional rites
- Eastern liturgies
- Western liturgies
- liturgical books
- Latin
- chant

REFLECT

- What does the ancient axiom *lex orandi, lex credendi* mean to me?
- Do I treat the Church's liturgy as something primarily for God, or something primarily for my own information, edification, or entertainment?
- Do I see *traditional* rites as the only inherently sacred rites in the Church? Do I frequent these rites?

DISCUSS

- With regard to the Church's sacred rites, do you have the same conviction of St. Teresa of Ávila, mentioned in this chapter? Why or why not?
- Describe a time when you or someone you know were especially impacted by the beauty or holiness of Latin, Gregorian chant, or any particular Catholic rite.
- Do you frequent the traditional Roman Rite—either of Mass, or the other sacraments and sacramentals? If not, why not? If so, would you agree that they support the Church's unity and mission, rather than hinder them?

LEX CREDENDI

"The liturgy is primarily for the glorification of God. In a connected but secondary way, it is also a source of instruction and sanctification for those who participate in it. Why is the liturgy essential to the Church? Because the Church was established to offer right worship. It continues the work of Our Lord, the eternal High Priest, 'prolong[ing] the priestly mission of Jesus Christ mainly by means of the sacred liturgy.'" — *Credo*, 312

LEX ORANDI

"The hour cometh, and now is, when the true adorers shall adore the Father in spirit and in truth. For the Father also seeketh such to adore Him. God is a spirit; and they that adore Him, must adore Him in spirit and in truth." — Gospel, Friday in the Third Week of Lent

Part III, Chapter 16: Sacred Space

STUDY

- sacred space
- church buildings
- architectural styles
- bells
- cemeteries
- catacombs

REFLECT

- I will thank God for the consecrated space that is geographically closest to me.
- Have I ever prayed or contributed to the construction or beautification of a sacred place? Why or why not?
- Do I say a prayer for the poor souls, whenever I pass a cemetery? Why or why not?

DISCUSS

- Have you ever attended the solemn consecration of a church, chapel, oratory, bell, or cemetery? What was it like?
- What is your favorite Catholic architectural style, and why?
- How would you respond with clarity and charity to someone who was considering cremation over bodily burial?

"Are all places equally holy, since God is present everywhere? No. Throughout time, God has manifested His presence in specific places, making them particularly holy. At first, the divine apparition directly sanctified a place.... With the establishment of the Old Law, the tabernacle and temple became the locus of holiness.... [And] by establishing the sacraments, especially the Holy Sacrifice of the Mass, Jesus determined that God would be particularly worshipped wherever the sacraments would be offered, which in turn would sanctify those places." — *Credo*, 318

LEX ORANDI

"O God, Who dost invisibly contain all things, and yet dost visibly show the signs of Thy power for the salvation of mankind, illumine this temple by the virtue of Thine indwelling, and grant that all who assemble here to pray, from whatsoever tribulation they shall call upon Thee, may obtain the blessings of Thy consolation." —Collect, Dedication of a Church

Part III, Chapter 17: Sacred Objects

STUDY

- altar
- liturgical vessels
- chalice linens
- liturgical substances
- ecclesiastical garb
- sacred vestments

REFLECT

- I will meditate on God's establishment of stone altars for His own divine worship.
- Do I properly reverence the altar at my local church?
- What "sacred object" in Catholic life has the greatest significance for me?

DISCUSS

- Describe an impressive tabernacle-and-altar combination that you have seen in the past. What most struck you about its appearance?
- Non-Catholics are sometimes confused about why the Church uses so much "sacred stuff" in her liturgy. How would you respond?
- Share something that you learned for the first time about the spiritual symbolism behind the liturgical object(s) described in this chapter.

"What is an *altar*? In the strictly liturgical sense, it is a consecrated stone upon which the host and chalice are placed during the celebration of Holy Mass.... Who has the power to consecrate altars? The bishop alone, although the Church may grant this power to priests at need; e.g., missionaries in areas where there are no bishops." — *Credo*, 321–322

LEX ORANDI

"Almighty, eternal God, sanctify by the power of Thy heavenly blessing this altar, dedicated to Thy name, and show the blessing of Thine assistance unto all who hope in Thee, that both the power of the sacraments and the effect thereof may here be obtained." —Postcommunion, Consecration of an Altar

Part III, Chapter 18: Sacred Time

STUDY

- sacred time
- liturgical year
- civic feasts
- religious feasts
- temporal cycle
- sanctoral cycle

REFLECT

- I will thank God for establishing sacred time and the Church's wise order of feasts and fasts.
- Which liturgical season draws me closest to Jesus Christ? Why?
- Which feast will I observe with greater attention this year? What additional custom or devotional practice will I adopt for this purpose?

DISCUSS

- What does it mean to say that "the liturgical year *is Christ*"?
- Which liturgical season or feast is your favorite? Why?
- Share something that you learned in this chapter about the liturgical year that you didn't know before.

LEX CREDENDI

"What is the liturgical year? The Church's annual cycle of feasts and fasts, unfolding 'the whole mystery of Christ, from the Incarnation and Birth until the Ascension, the day of Pentecost, and the expectation of blessed hope and of the Coming of the Lord.' In summary, 'the liturgical year is Christ always living in His Church.'" — *Credo*, 328

LEX ORANDI

"It is truly meet and just, right and profitable, to extol Thee indeed at all times, O Lord, but chiefly with highest praise to magnify Thee on this day on which for us was sacrificed Christ, our Pasch. For He is the true Lamb Who hath taken away the sins of the world; Who by dying Himself hath destroyed our death; and by rising again hath bestowed a new life on us." — Preface, Easter Sunday

Part III, Chapter 19: Devotions

STUDY

- devotions
- pilgrimage
- devotions to Christ (Passion, Holy Childhood, Blessed Sacrament, Sacred Heart, Holy Face, Holy Name)
- devotions to Mary (First Saturdays, Rosary, Angelus, brown scapular, miraculous medal, consecration)
- associations
- third orders

REFLECT

- I will thank God for the gift of knowing Him, and of being devoted to Him.
- If devotion is an outward expression of love, could a stranger identify me as someone devoted to Christ and His Church? Why or why not?
- Am I sufficiently devoted to the cause of Christ and His Kingdom? Do I work to promote it? Do I fight to defend it?

DISCUSS

- Describe your favorite form of "popular piety," and why it appeals to you.
- Making pilgrimage is one of the most ancient forms of devotion, dating back to Old Testament times; describe a pilgrimage that you or someone you know experienced.
- Explain how you show devotion to your own guardian angel or patron saints.

LEX CREDENDI

"What is the purpose of all devotion—indeed, of the entire Christian life? To gain many graces by the mercy of God and intercession of His saints, and to train ourselves toward spiritual perfection; that we may better know, love, and serve God in this life, so to be happy with Him forever in the next. 'Fear God, and keep His commandments: for this is all' (Eccles 12:13)." — *Credo*, 340

LEX ORANDI

"Hear, O Lord, we beseech Thee, the prayers of those who humbly pray together; guard and continually defend those who with devout hearts worship Thee, that we may not be hindered by any trouble, but may always freely serve Thee." —Collect, Mass for Conferring Holy Orders

NOTES

NOTES

NOTES

NOTES

NOTES

NOTES

NOTES

NOTES

Sophia Institute

Sophia Institute is a nonprofit institution that seeks to nurture the spiritual, moral, and cultural life of souls and to spread the gospel of Christ in conformity with the authentic teachings of the Roman Catholic Church.

Sophia Institute Press fulfills this mission by offering translations, reprints, and new publications that afford readers a rich source of the enduring wisdom of mankind.

Sophia Institute also operates the popular online Catholic resource CatholicExchange.com. *Catholic Exchange* provides world news from a Catholic perspective as well as daily devotionals and articles that will help readers to grow in holiness and live a life consistent with the teachings of the Church.

In 2013, Sophia Institute launched Sophia Institute for Teachers to renew and rebuild Catholic culture through service to Catholic education. With the goal of nurturing the spiritual, moral, and cultural life of souls, and an abiding respect for the role and work of teachers, we strive to provide materials and programs that are at once enlightening to the mind and ennobling to the heart; faithful and complete, as well as useful and practical.

Sophia Institute gratefully recognizes the Solidarity Association for preserving and encouraging the growth of our apostolate over the course of many years. Without their generous and timely support, this book would not be in your hands.

www.SophiaInstitute.com
www.CatholicExchange.com
www.SophiaInstituteforTeachers.org

Sophia Institute Press° is a registered trademark of Sophia Institute.
Sophia Institute is a tax-exempt institution as defined by the
Internal Revenue Code, Section 501(c)(3). Tax I.D. 22-2548708.